CW00859536

WHERE THE DEEP ONES ARE

STORY BY KENNETH HITE • PICTURES BY ANDY HOPP
EDITING & LAYOUT BY MICHELLE NEPHEW

ATLAS GAMES, PUBLISHER
WWW.ATLAS-GAMES.COM

ISBN-10 1-58978-103-1
ISBN-13 987-1-58978-103-0

When Bobby would yell for seconds on fish

and thirds

his mother said his big mouth would give him brain fever
like his cousin Larry Marsh and how would he like that?

and Bobby said just fine

and his mother sent him to his room without any fish at all.

That very night in Bobby's room he heard rushing water

and it got louder
and louder

until it washed away his walls

and a river ran right through his room
carrying an old boat barely dry
just for Bobby

and he sailed down the river
and under wooden bridges
and past tumbled walls

to Innsmouth.

SUMATRA QUEEN

Innsmouth smelled a lot like fish
and it even had a fish on the church

but when Bobby tried to go there, an old man told him "No! That's where the DEEP ONES are!"

"The Deep Ones never die."

“They came from the South Seas with Captain Marsh and took over the church”

"and they gave Deep One gold to all the pretty girls in town and took them dancing under the ocean in a wild rumpus"

“and nobody ever saw the girls again.”

Bobby said, “My cousin’s name is Larry Marsh.”

**and after that the old man got "skeert"
and wouldn't talk to Bobby any more.**

But Bobby still smelled fish, so he went to the hotel for dinner.
The bread was bad and the soup was bad and even the water was bad

but there was plenty of fish. Bobby ate so much he got sleepy and slow and then the Deep Ones came for him.

The Deep Ones croaked their terrible croaks and smacked their terrible lips

and rolled their terrible eyes
and waved their terrible flippers

and Bobby ran out of the hotel and through Eliot Street and down Bates Street and across Fall Street and even past Devil's Reef

and just when Bobby thought he was lost for good he found the river.

Bobby jumped in the old boat
and sailed up the river
and past tumbled walls
and under wooden bridges

and back into his very own room.

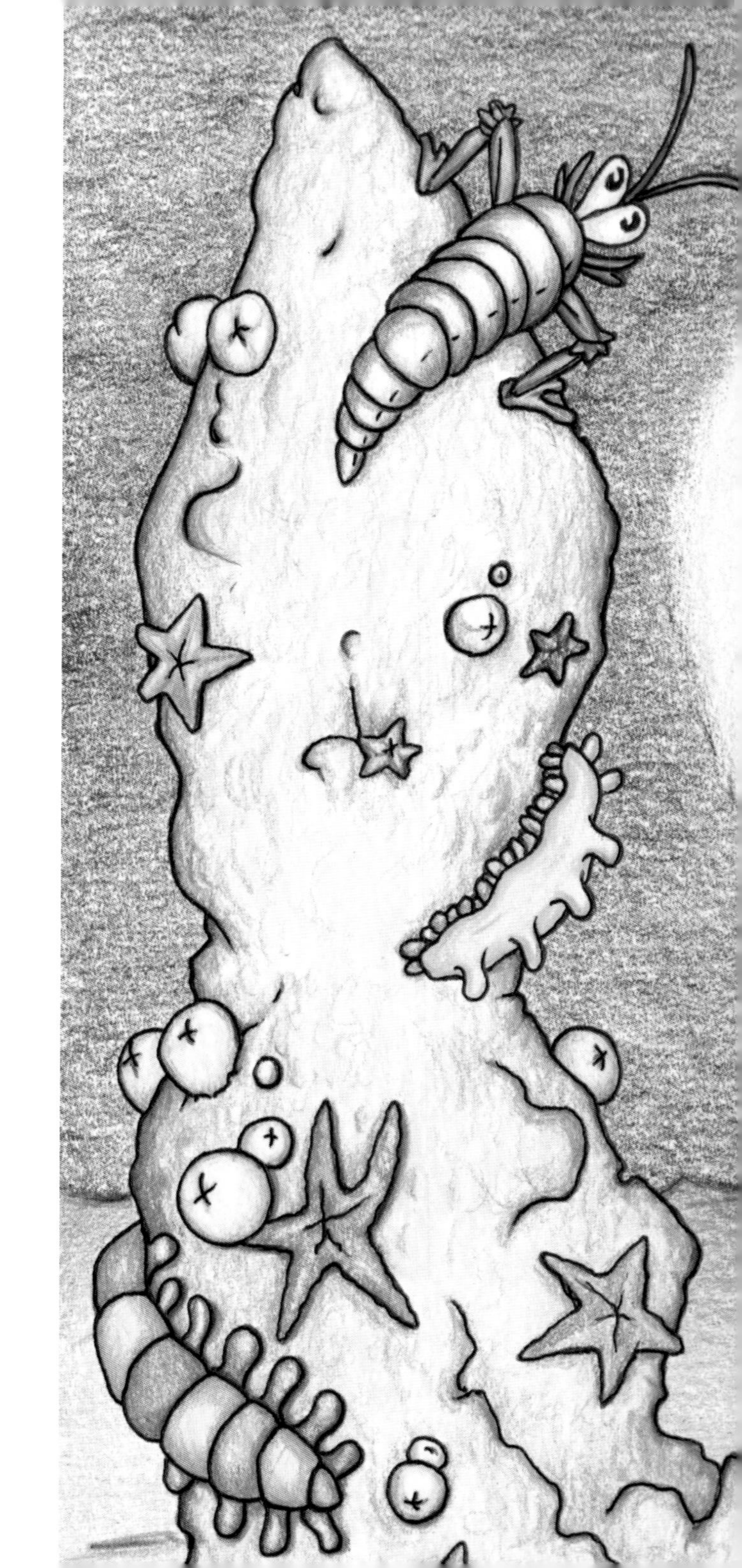

But he was still hungry for fish.

So Bobby thought he might go visit his cousin Larry Marsh
and find another old boat

and they would sail under the wooden bridges
and past the tumbled walls
and back down to Innsmouth

and the Deep Ones would call him the most Deep One of all

and crown him with Deep One gold
and make him king of all Deep Ones

and he would dance with the pretty girls of Innsmouth
under the ocean in a wild rumpus

and never die

**and he would eat all the fish he wanted
and anything else too.**